Thomas Telford's
SCOTLAND

Chris Morris

AUTHOR'S NOTE

This book is a visual celebration of Thomas Telford's engineering and architecture in his home country of Scotland. It contains material first used in On Tour with Thomas Telford, *published in 2004, with subsequent photography taken in 2006 and 2009.*

First published 2009 by Tanners Yard Press

Tanners Yard Press Church Road Longhope GL17 0LA
www.tannersyardpress.co.uk

British Library Cataloguing in Publication Data
A catalogue record for this book is available from the British Library

ISBN 978-09542096-9-8

Designed by Paul Manning
Printed and bound in Poland
Polskabook UK Ltd

*Front cover image: Craigellachie Bridge over the Spey
Facing and previous page: Plaque of Thomas Telford,
Westerkirk Library, Bentpath (NY 308900)*

Contents

'It is more by the performance of useful works than the enjoyment
of splendid orders I wish my name to be known'

Thomas Telford, on hearing that he had been knighted
by the King of Sweden

INTRODUCTION

Thomas Telford was one of the giants of his age, a man of boundless energy and intellectual curiosity who through his achievements helped to define the nineteenth century as the heroic age of engineering. The first President of the Institution of Civil Engineers, Telford more than any other established engineering as a profession. Two hundred years later, today's engineers would find his practices familiar: his ability to design, specify and delegate and to put together and rely upon a team of trained and trusted surveyors, foremen and masons. In this way his prolific output could be translated into the abundance of great works that span the country and by which we now recognise and revere him.

In this book Chris Morris brings to life through his vivid portfolio of photographs the bold inventiveness of a man whose genius can be appreciated as much for its elegance and artistry as its engineering vigour. At the time of their building Telford's works commanded awe and esteem. They conferred certainty on the emerging world of industrial and mercantile prosperity by forging the essential links on which trade and commerce could depend. And they fuelled the debate on the sublime and the picturesque which absorbed the attentions of contemporary writers and artists.

His proliferation of works is nowhere more obvious than in Scotland. Of the Caledonian Canal, which he visited with Telford in 1819, Robert Southey wrote: 'Here we see the powers of nature brought to act upon a great scale, in subservience to the purposes of men.' Their Scottish tour was a great success, a pleasant incident in the lives of two busy men, both at the height of their careers – Southey as Poet Laureate, Telford the pre-eminent civil engineer of his generation. Southey observed with unqualified approval the civilising and beneficial value of good roads and bridges on the people and economy of Scotland and applauded Telford for the scale and nature of his achievements.

Telford's roads, bridges, canals and harbours demonstrate clearly and powerfully the triumph of mankind over nature in the interests of creating a universal good. It is this absence of ambiguity that sets Telford's works apart. Their spirit of unbridled self-confidence is as compelling today as when they were built, a generation or more before the horrors of industrialisation that have clouded our view of the middle years of the nineteenth century. A passage through the Caledonian or Gotha canals or along the Welsh section of the Holyhead Road exhilarates as no other. But if at the time Telford was affirming a mastery over the physical world, today his works, softened by time and nature, enjoy an extraordinary affinity with the landscapes of which they form part. Almost without exception his engineering design complements rather than despoils. If there are exceptions, they were never built. His proposal for spanning the Avon Gorge in Bristol – with 'Gothic' towers rising from the water's edge – is difficult to take seriously, whereas what is arguably his masterpiece, the crossing of the straits of Menai, must stand as one of the great works of art and engineering of all time. In his cast-iron bridges, too, Telford achieved grace, style and economy, perfecting at Bonar, at the head of Dornoch Firth, a design he was to use on several occasions again, notably in the spectacular setting of Craigellachie.

Throughout, Chris Morris draws on detail to emphasise Telford's sensitivity to setting and place. His photographs demonstrate clearly that there was more to Telford than meets the eye. And what he has captured so beautifully here meets the eye in a most seemly manner. It is a prelude to the tour that must follow.

Neil Cossons,
former Chairman, English Heritage

Tongland bridge (NX 692533), on the Stanraer road, was Telford's first major bridge in Scotland since Langholm.

I

THOMAS TELFORD'S SCOTLAND

From the humblest of origins Thomas Telford rose to become the pre-eminent engineer of his age. Trained as a stonemason, in the last decade of the eighteenth century he took iron, the new material, and made himself master of its structural possibilities.

Leaving aside his initial apprenticeships in Langholm and Edinburgh, Telford's work in Scotland divides into two main groups: the majority comprises harbour, road and bridge-building, directly commissioned by the Westminster-sponsored British Fisheries Association, and various road commissions. In addition are the designs for churches and manses for the Church of Scotland. All these add up to a large body of work, full of visual interest, but they are hardly the reputation-making, groundbreaking achievements of a man whose fame has lasted a quarter of a millennium. Quite separately there is the major engineering triumph of the Caledonian Canal.

While the fishery and church schemes seem of little engineering significance, the whole programme reveals Telford's social commitment to his native country. This contention would seem validated by the fact that he took no fee from the Fisheries Society for his harbour work and his willingness to design for the Church; a fair comparison might be to wonder what high-flying architect would today design forty village halls?

Although his two 'wonders of the world' (Pontcysyllte aqueduct and Menai bridge) are in Wales, a tour of Scotland in Telford's footsteps is nevertheless an exciting prospect, for a layman as well as an engineer. No one could fail to be moved by the sight of the elegant iron span of Craigellachie bridge leaping across the Spey, or from the road above Loy, the first glance of the Caledonian Canal snaking its way into the Great Glen, its broad waterway dwarfed by the terrific landscape. There are many other sights to marvel at, from the massive stonework of the east coast harbours to the tiny churches often found in the wildest locations. But in addition there is the knowledge that the author of all these works was not merely fulfilling a contract but attempting to do his bit for the betterment of mankind. As Sir Neil Cossons, former chairman of English Heritage, has said, Telford was not just working at the time of the Enlightenment, but was himself a part of that movement.

Early days

Thomas Telford was born in 1757 in an isolated cottage in the Scottish border country. Within months his father, a shepherd, had died. It is difficult to imagine a tougher start in life. With the help of an uncle, Telford attended parish school. The benefit of an education was matched by the lasting friendships he made which served him throughout his life.

On leaving school Telford was apprenticed to a stonemason in Langholm and developed an ambition to become an architect. He furthered his prospects with a spell in Edinburgh's burgeoning New Town before moving south. It would be some twenty years before he returned to country of his birth, by then a man of reputation and influence, and with the tag of a new profession to his name – engineer.

Harbours and new towns

After the abortive rise of Bonnie Prince Charlie in 1745, the English army under Cumberland and Wade had ruthlessly crushed Scotland and destroyed the clan system, the social fabric of the Highlands. Fifty years later, London finally decided that rural Scotland, decimated and destitute, needed radical assistance and sponsored the British Fisheries Society, whose plan was to regenerate the Highland economy by encouraging fishing. One of the Society members was Telford's childhood friend and subsequent patron, William Pultney, who asked him to be involved in building harbours.

The Caledonian Canal at Fort Augustus, with Loch Ness in the background (NH 377092)

Unloading crabs at Gourdon Harbour

It was Pultney's invitation in 1796 which re-involved Telford with the country of his birth. Most of the harbour works were on the east coast where, frequently, fishermen were still hauling their boats up on unprotected beaches; Telford's answer was often a single jetty, providing mooring, shelter and easier unloading of the catch. In some cases improvements were made to existing facilities, sometimes on a very different scale, as at Aberdeen and Peterhead.

Three of the harbour works extended to a wider brief. The Society had planned new towns at Ullapool and Tobermory before Telford's involvement, but he offered subsequent advice to both schemes. Uniquely at Wick he had a project of his own, to plan a new settlement south of the harbour. Named Pultneytown, in addition to its well-planned residential spaces, it included what has been claimed as the first industrial estate, with workshops for all the trades associated with the fishing industry. By the late nineteenth century Wick became a prosperous town, but only fascinating fragments of Pultneytown survive today.

Roads and bridges

It was rapidly perceived that helping fishermen by improving their harbours would lead to nothing if the herring catch could not reach its markets. Wade's military roads were the nearest thing to a network but they were in bad repair, and anyway tended to suit armies marching from the south rather than fishermen wanting to trade inland. Thus an ambitious road-building programme was undertaken which saw Telford plan and engineer something approaching a thousand miles of road, linking the far north east and west coasts with the lowlands, and on to England. This included the need for hundreds of bridges, some inconsequential and others grand statements such as at Dunkeld, over the Tay, and the Dean Bridge in Edinburgh.

Iron does not feature greatly in Telford's work in Scotland. Apart from the swing-bridges on the Canal, the beautiful span at Craigellachie and a long-lost one at Bonar, all his bridge work was in stone. While we can think of iron as being the new material he took and used to perfection, it is instructive to note the progress of masonry design. Even in his first Scottish bridge, Tongland, he used the technique of internal bracing walls, rather than rubble infill, for strength with lightness.

Cartland Crags bridge, Lanark (NS 868444)

All this work in Scotland fitted in with his many other commitments. Despite local supervision (and one of his strengths was picking able men for his team) at least once a year Telford undertook a Highland tour to check on progress personally. With thousands of miles to cover on horseback or pony-trap no-one could be better qualified to realise the need for the better road network for which he was responsible.

The Caledonian Canal

The exception to this massive bundling together of fairly humble work was the Caledonian Canal. This project, spanning the years 1802 to 1822, is a singular major achievement, the fruit of vision and perseverance (despite the fact that by 1840 it was nearly closed down, not being deep enough for the increasing size of ships).

It only takes a glance at a map of the Highlands to see the fault line lying between Fort William and Inverness; contained in this natural valley, the Great Glen, are the three lochs, Lochy, Oich and Ness, emptying to the sea at Loch Lynne and Beauly Firth. A waterway connecting the coasts might look an easy project, but that would be far from the truth: the lochs were at very different heights, and in places surprisingly shallow with hard rock beds. The engineering difficulties can be exemplified by the building of the sea locks at each end: that at Corpach, on Loch Lynne, had to be cut out of solid rock, while at Clachnaharry, the north-west exit to Beauly Firth, the masonry had to be built up from a deep bed of soft mud.

For nearly two hundred years the Caledonian Canal has been flagged up as one of Telford's great triumphs. While he was the man above all others who planned and saw it through to completion, it would be wrong to ignore the genesis of the project. The first to report on the possibility of a waterway through the Great Glen was James Watt, of steam engine fame, who made a survey in 1773 for a consortium of landowners. When Telford took on the task for the government in 1802, he consulted Watt before making his own report. Meanwhile another great engineer of the late nineties, John Rennie, had made a new survey in 1793, probably for the Fisheries Board, for whom Telford was to work extensively and who had been long-time advocates of a canal. When preliminary works for construction began in 1803, it was William Jessop who was appointed as consulting engineer and up to his death in 1814 he and Telford worked hand

in glove on the Caledonian. Stangely Jessop gets no mention in Telford's autobiography – a fact discussed on page 78. As well as the Caledonian, Telford was involved with the Crinan and with the Edinburgh & Glasgow Union canals.

Churches

Following the conclusion of the Napoleonic wars, the Westminster government, presumably grateful to God who it is supposed supports the winning side, allocated a grant to the Church of England for new building work. Almost as an afterthought a much smaller sum was offered to the Church of Scotland, who dedicated it to a series of outlying churches and manses in parishes either too poor to build for themselves or with a such a scattered congregation that extra churches were needed.

Telford was asked to advise on this project and designed a standard plan, with the choice of a one- or two-storey manse. Today, many of the thirty-two churches and forty manses have been altered and some are in private ownership, but they still convey the pattern of the original design. Fitting in with the criteria of need, inevitably all the parishes are in the Highlands and islands; discovering these churches, often in wild and dramatic locations, makes for a rewarding tour.

Facing page: Crinan Canal; above: Acharacle church, west of Ballachulish

2

THE BORDERS, LOWLANDS AND ISLAY

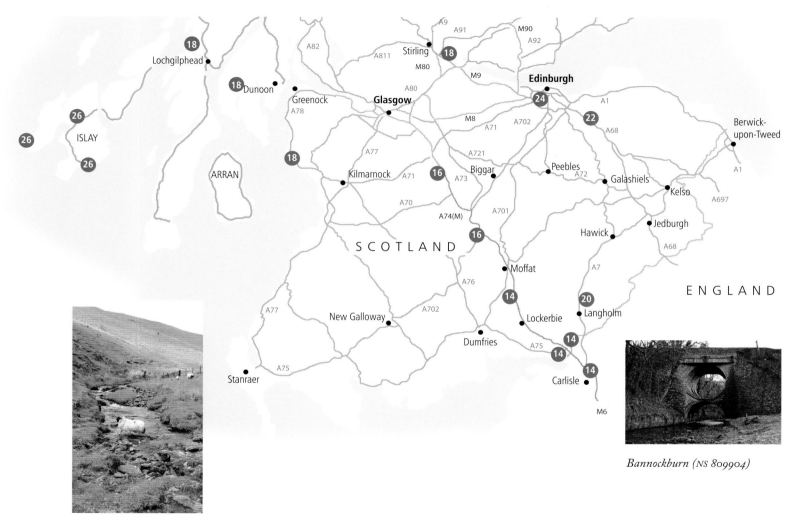

18 Lochgilphead

18 Dunoon

18 Stirling

18 Edinburgh 24

22 Berwick-upon-Tweed

26 ISLAY

26

26

18 Greenock Glasgow Kilmarnock Peebles Galashiels Kelso

ARRAN

A82

A811

M80

M9

A80

Glasgow

A78

M8

A71

A702

A1

A68

A77

A71

A721

16 Biggar

A73

A72

A701

A70

A74(M)

16 Hawick Jedburgh

A68

A7

SCOTLAND

Moffat

A76

20 Langholm

ENGLAND

A77

14 Lockerbie

New Galloway

A702

14

14

A75

Dumfries

A75 Carlisle

14

M6

Stanraer

Sheep at Glendinning (NY 299969)

Bannockburn (NS 809904)

13

In 1814 works were planned to replace the old turnpike road, which had become virtually impassable. In 1825 the new road was complete; the change has been likened by the historian Roland Paxton to the construction of a new motorway today. In fact Telford's 'new' road is totally bypassed by today's A74(M), and still exists in its entirety as a quiet alternative.

Right: A remnant of the iron bridge over the Esk stands in the garden of Tully House Museum, Carlisle.

Top right: Typical bridge at Ecclefechan, with the modern road behind.

Below left and right: The only remaining milestone stands by a farm building at Dinwoodie Green (lovingly painted red by the farmer). The fine toll house at Dinwoodie is almost hidden by high hedges, and is represented here by its brass letterbox!

Facing page: Gretna is the first of eight toll houses on the road.

GLASGOW ROAD, NORTH END

*Facing page: Close to the road's
1,000-ft summit at Beattock,
Telford designed a coaching inn and
stables. The nearby bridge is almost
hidden in its tree-choked ravine but
its centre roundel is in view (below
left), replaced on the road side of
the parapet.*

*Right: Elvanfoot bridge crosses a
headwater of the Clyde on a
windswept moor.*

*Below right: A tollhouse stands
abandoned beside the fine bridge
at Hamilton.*

Right: Telford's Ardrossan harbour is now home to a marina.

Below left: Further north, on Bute, sections of the Glendaruel road remain.

Facing page and below right: The Crinan Canal was not built by Telford, but it was he who in 1816 supervised remedial work to correct original poor-quality contracting.

The son of a shepherd, Telford was born at Glendinning, in the valley of Meggat Water, an isolated area of tumbling streams and high sheep pasture north-west of Langholm. His early work includes a gravestone for his father (right), in the burial ground of Westerkirk church at Bentpath.

Below: In the town itself, a stone doorway was probably made as a training exercise.

Facing page: Boys throw stones into the Esk at Langholm Bridge where Telford worked as an apprentice mason in 1775.

Telford took enormous trouble to keep his roads straight and level. The impressive Pathead viaduct (facing page and detail, below right) crosses the Tynewater valley ten miles south of Edinburgh, but a much smaller bridge, involving neither a detour nor steep gradients, would have sufficed.

To keep the road level at Falla, just to the south, a massive embankment fills the valley of the Dean Burn, with the stream diverted into a tunnel (right).

A comparison of a detail of Pathead with the gothic pedestrian/flood arch at Tongland, built twenty years earlier (right), shows how Telford developed the visual appearance of his bridges. The double radius arches at Pathead give a light effect, a design shared with Dean bridge in Edinburgh (see page 24).

Right: A boy fishes for brown trout in the Waters of Leith, beneath Dean Bridge.

Crossing the same river is the Slateford aqueduct (facing page) on the Edinburgh & Glasgow Union canal, one of three similar ones using iron troughs. Telford, consultant to the project, saw no need to encase the iron with masonry but his advice was ignored.

Top right: Emeritus Professor Roland Paxton has a collection of Telford items at his archives in Heriot-Watt University. On display behind him is an original link from the Menai Bridge.

Below: Fishermen's boats on the Glencouse Reservoir, built in 1820 for the city's water supply; Telford was consultant for the dam construction.

Of the three sites on Islay, Risabus (top right) is a ruin, while Kilmeny (right) and Portnahaven (facing page) are thriving parish churches.

Below: Members of the Board of Congregation are photographed inside Portnahaven's church. Telford's standard plan of two entrances is put to a particular use here, with one doorway used by the host village and the other by the adjoining community of Port Wemyss.

3
THE HIGHLANDS, GREAT GLEN AND MULL

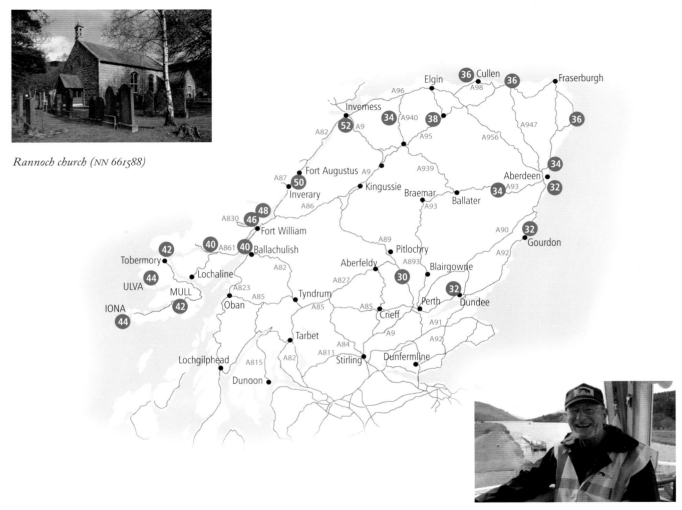

Rannoch church (NN 661588)

Inverness
Elgin **36** Cullen
A98
Fraserburgh
36
A96
34 A940 **38** **36**
52 A9
A82 A95
A947
A956
Fort Augustus A9
A939
A87
50 Kingussie
Inverary Braemar Aberdeen **34**
A86 **34** A93 **32**
48 A93 Ballater
46
A830 Fort William A90 **32**
40 A861 **40** Ballachulish A89 Pitlochry Gourdon
42 A82 A92
Tobermory Aberfeldy A893 Blairgowrie
44 Lochaline A827 **30**
ULVA MULL **32**
42 Oban Tyndrum Perth Dundee
IONA A85 A85 Crieff
44 A85 A91
Tarbet A9 A92
A84
Lochgilphead A815 A82 A811 Stirling Dunfermline
Dunoon

Norman Hill, *bridge keeper, Aberchalder*
(2004) (NH 337035)

29

DUNKELD

*One of Telford's earliest Highland
bridges, from 1804, Dunkeld (right
and detail, below) replaced a
hazardous ferry over the Tay. Its
original toll house (facing page) is
on the south side.*

Birnam
Walk

The remains of Telford's harbour work at Dundee now forms part of the Discovery Point leisure zone (below).

Facing page: Gourdon is a rare example of a small harbour still working in the traditional way. Douglas Welsh has lived in the village all his life. His business includes everything from catching, curing and smoking fish to marketing.

Right: Aberdeen already had a large harbour, but Telford's extension of the North Pier (seen here with a pilot vessel bringing in an oil rig supply ship) provided shelter to the whole bay.

HIGHLAND BRIDGES

The bridges at Aberdeen over the Don (below), at Potarch over the Dee (facing page), and at Ferness over the Findhorn (right) are three of many associated with Telford's road-building programme.

Most of Telford's improvements were simple stone-built jetties to provide mooring and shelter for small fishing boats. Cullen (right) is an unaltered example. Banff (facing page) has had more quays added.

Below: Peterhead has been hugely altered. This old lighthouse marked an original entrance.

Although Telford was a skilled mason, it was his use of iron that made him famous. This bridge, shining bright against its wooded hill as it soars over the Spey, exemplifies the lightness of structure that must have dazzled the world two centuries ago.

CHURCHES BY LOCH LINNHE

*Facing page and top right:
Duror and its manse (below right)
are south of the estuary on the
Oban road.*

*Just across Corran Ferry there is a
church at Ardgour (right), and
further west another at Acharacle
(see page 11).*

*Below: North of Ballahulisch at
Onich, the church has vanished but
the manse survives.*

MULL

The pretty harbour town of Tobermory (facing page) was a 1790s new town originally planned by the British Fisheries Society. Telford became involved later, offering advice on the quality of the harbour stonework. He also advised against further cutting away of the cliff, instead recommending housing on the higher level at Breadalbane Street (right).

Mull boasts three rare two-storey manses: in Tobermory (below), at Salen (below right) and – reputedly the best – at Kinlochspelvie, where there is also a recently altered church (below, far right).

Famous for its ancient monastery and as a cradle of British Christianity, Iona has a Telford church (facing page) and a single-storey manse (below right) used as a visitor centre.

Ulva, a remote island off the west coast of Mull, has a surviving church (right, and below left), but with no services or congregation it is hard to maintain. The Rt. Hon. Mrs J.M. Howard (right), who owns the church and the island, lives in the original single-storey manse close by.

Just north of Fort William is the Caledonian Canal's most famous feature, the flight of locks at Banavie known as Neptune's Staircase.

Far right: An RNLI boat ascends the flight en route from Islay to Buckie. The white house (below, right) was Telford's residence during his visits.

At the top of the flight the view across the canal is towards Ben Nevis (facing page). The Mucomer Cut (right) is a channel taking surplus water away from Loch Lochy.

The only original swing bridge on the Caldenonian Canal is at Moy (right and facing page). The bridge is split, pivoting from each bank. Bridge keeper Andrew Walker keeps the southern wing open, closing it as needed for farm traffic; when a large boat requires the whole canal width, he has to row over to open the north section.

Below: One mile west, the aqueduct at Loy with its heavy masonry tunnels for farm traffic and for the river passage underlines the lightness of Moy's iron structure.

At Laggan Lock the Caledonian Canal reaches its summit level. The white building (right) is the original lock-keeper's house. To the north-west is the Laggan Cutting (facing page), its depth disguised by a plantation of Scots pines.

Beyond, the canal joins Loch Oich. This summit level – indeed, the whole canal – is supplied by water from the river Garry (below).

At the north end of Loch Oich, the Aberchalder swing bridge (below right) is the last feature before the canal reaches Fort Augustus where a flight of locks drop into Loch Ness.

CALEDONIAN CANAL, NORTH END

The River Ness exits the Loch at its north end over a weir (right), which raises the water level in Loch Ness and Loch Dochfour.

Bona lighthouse (top right) helps ships navigate into the canal exit. These features were kindly pointed out to the author by Mike and 'DJ' of British Waterways (below).

Facing page: At Clachnaharry, at the north east end of the canal, the sea lock opens out into the Beauly Firth .

4
THE FAR NORTH AND SKYE

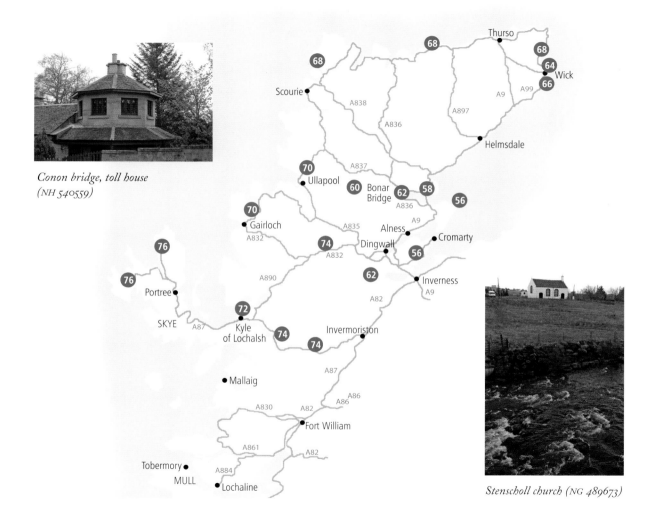

Conon bridge, toll house
(NH 540559)

Stenscholl church (NG 489673)

Thurso
68
68
64
Wick
66
A99
A9
Scourie
A838
A897
A836
Helmsdale
A837
70
Ullapool
60 Bonar
Bridge
62 58
56
A836
A9
70
Alness
56
Gairloch
A835
Cromarty
A832
74
Dingwall
56
A832
62
Inverness
76
A890
A9
76
Portree
A82
72
Invermoriston
SKYE A87
Kyle
of Lochalsh
74
74
A87
Mallaig
A86
A86
A830
A82
Fort William
A861
A82
Tobermory
MULL A884
Lochaline

As further south, simple jetties predominate, unaltered at Fortrose (right) and Portmahomack (facing page).

Invergordon (below) is now a huge oil rig repair yard, but sections of Telford's stone-built quays are still visible. Captain Iain Dunderdale has 'Deputy Harbour Master' on his hard hat but 'Cruise Development Manager' on his business card. Tourists call in to marvel at the rigs en route to search for Loch Ness monsters.

Fleet Mound (facing page) is a causeway built across the Dornoch Firth, cutting twenty miles off the main road north.

The project was conceived by the Duke of Sutherland as a way of reclaiming agricultural land, and Telford was called in to help make it work. At the north end of the embankment (right), he installed arches allowing tidal flow, which was controlled by sluices.

Below: One of the two original controlling winches is on view at the 'History Links' museum in Dornoch.

CROIK

Croik church (right), ten miles west of Bonar Bridge, is worth a diversion, as it bears unique witness to the mass clearances of the early nineteenth century, when tenant farmers were evicted from the land and their homes to make way for more profitable sheep-farming.

Telford's church was built in 1823 and has not been altered since. In 1845 eighteen dispossessed families who were huddled in the churchyard, scratched desperate messages on the east window of the church (facing page). Some of the inscriptions read:

> *'Glencalvie people the wicked generation'*

> *'Glencalvie tenants residing here'*

> *'Glencalvie people was in the churchyard here May 24 1845'*

The manse (top right) is the only other dwelling in this part of Glencalvie.

Right: Peter Wilde, assistant curator of the 'History Links' museum in Dornoch, shows a copy of a contemporary print of Bonar Bridge.

Far right: Easter Fearn, just south of Dornoch Firth.

Facing page: Fisherman at Lovat, on the Beauly river.

WICK

Telford built a bridge in Wick, since replaced, and a harbour, some of whose enormous stonework survives (right). More importantly he planned a complete new town, named after his patron, William Pultney.

It is claimed that Pultneytown included the world's first industrial estate; certainly the planned spaces allowed for herring-gutting and curing yards (facing page) as well as workshops for all the trades associated with the fishing industry. Workers' housing, conveniently close to the harbour, was part of the mix.

A heritage centre by the harbour keeps old memories alive, while projected renovations include Telford Street (right).

Telford's plan for Pultneytown centred on Argyll Square, an elegant oval filled with sycamores (facing page). Beyond now-replaced housing were more industrial spaces, including a ropeworks (below right).

Pultneytown brought prosperity to the far north, but later its luck changed and in 1903 it was incorporated into Wick. In 1940 some of the first German bombs fell on the harbour. Is this the only British town still with unrepaired war damage? In 1971 the council were advised to demolish most of the housing of Pultneytown, but fascinating fragments remain.

Top right: Tony Sinclair, a director of the Wick heritage centre, has a story about the roundhouse (behind him in the photo). Built by Telford as a single-storey dwelling, it was bought by a Mr Bremner (a 'wreck-raiser') who found it too small. As an engineering experiment, he jacked up the whole stone-built house, roof and all, and added a new ground floor below!

FAR NORTH CHURCHES

Right: Berriedale, on a clifftop north of Helmsdale.

Below right: Keiss, north of Wick, also has a two-storey manse.

Below: Strathy, on the north coast.

Facing page: Kinlochbervie, high on the north-west tip of the Sutherland shoreline.

ULLAPOOL AND POOLEWE

Ullapool still has its Telford church (right), but his harbour work has been completely overtaken by modern developments. His suggestion to build a market place behind the quays was not taken up, but that is exactly where today's Saturday traders place their stalls (facing page). Behind the Loch Broom waterfront, Telford's advice to plan wide streets is very evident – a 'new town' style a hundred years ahead of its time.

Poolewe (below right) is south, down the long, lollopping roads of Wester Ross.

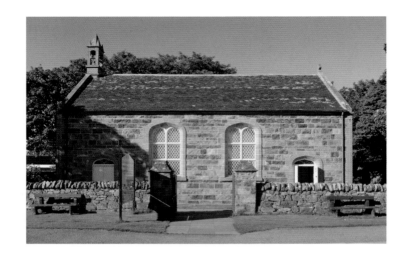

Facing page: Kinlochluikhart.

Right and below left: Plockton, north of Kyle of Lochalsh, and manse (below right).

Most of the routes of Telford's roads were so well chosen that they lie concealed under modern tarmac. However, on the A87 by Loch Cluanie (facing page) several sections of the original road are visible; where they are above the modern road, old stone block retaining walls can be seen.

Far right: The ruins of one of General Wade's military roads (built following the 1745 rebellion) leading into a Telford section, with the modern road beyond.

Shiel Bridge (right) is also on this route.

Facing page: Telford's church and manse stand together under a mountain at Stenscholl on the north east of Skye.

Right: To the west, on another northern peninsula, Hallin has a church, now disused, with a manse nextdoor (below).

Within a mile of Hallin, on the western shoreline, Telford planned a new settlement for the Fisheries Society. Known as Lochbay, the scheme never came to fruition, but some cottages in the hamlet of Stein date from that time.

5
TELFORD: A PLACE IN HISTORY

In my book on I.K. Brunel,* in an attempt to analyse the nature of his fame I compared him with other 'heroic' engineers of the early nineteenth century, including Telford. The most obvious comparison is with Robert Stephenson, Brunel's direct contemporary. Both sons of famous fathers, Brunel and Stephenson pushed the parameters of the nascent railway business. Perhaps Brunel's unlikely advantage in the fame game is the wonderful enduring photographic portrait by Robert Howlett, taken at the launch of the SS *Great Eastern*. I noted that Telford, from an earlier generation, despite neither the benefit of photography nor association with

the steam trains so beloved by the British public, still might be judged to have contributed more to the new profession of engineering which forged Britain's industrial revolution. There is a difference between fame and reputation.

So how did Telford fit into the pattern of engineering and engineers of his own time? Our perception of him is that he was a modest man, but one happy to receive praise for his achievements (see the quote on page 3). Telford was at his most inventive in his understanding of iron; he became the master of the use of this new material, and this is what underpins his reputation. When Abraham Darby built the Iron Bridge he conceived it as if built of timber – the castings fitted together with dovetail joints such as a cabinet-maker would use. Fifty years later the world had moved on and Telford's Menai suspension bridge had links tested to double the calculated required stress before approval for use. Of course this was in conjunction with William Hazeldine, the ironfounder whose works supplied almost all Telford's bridge castings.

Canal history in Britain dates back to James Brindley, who is credited with building the Duke of Bridgewater's coal-carrying canal to Manchester in 1761. Hard on his heels came John Smeaton, a prolific canal builder in the later decades of the eighteenth century, who has been called the 'first civil engineer'. Smeaton gave his name to the profession's first society, The Smeatonian, to which almost all the eminent engineers of the time belonged. In 1759 Smeaton took on William Jessop as an apprentice, thus giving a pedigree to the career of the man with whom in due course Telford would collaborate. In the last decade of the century, Jessop had become the pre-eminent canal and dock builder in Britain. Telford is also thought of as a founding father of the civil engineering profession; although he never joined the Smeatonian, he was elected first president of the Institution of Civil Engineers by his peers in 1818.

William Jessop had been appointed engineer to the Ellesmere canal in 1791, and it was almost two years before Telford joined his team. His convoluted job title was not definitive, but what seems likely is that the line of the canal, already laid out by Jessop, was honed down by Telford who, in particular was responsible for the spectacular Pontcysyllte aqueduct over the Dee. Jessop was a very busy man, concurrently building the Grand Junction (today's Grand Union) canal and West India docks, and may have been happy that his job was simply to approve Telford's initiatives.

In his autobiography, Telford conspicuously fails to make any mention of Jessop or of Jessop's involvement in both the Ellesmere and Caledonian canals. Is it possible that late in his life Telford's personality shifted, or that his judgement became clouded? Evidence to support this theory could come from Telford's action as government adviser in dismissing Brunel's design for the Clifton Bridge project in Bristol, with the contention that no suspension bridge could be longer than his own at Menai. Probably it was not Telford's intention to take all the glory for the work he shared with Jessop but, isolated and lonely in his old age, he allowed himself to write his 'life' from selective memory rather than rigorously looking back over the papers. In his will he appointed John Rickman, the secretary of the Caledonian Canal board, to be his executor and charged him with editing the book; this took several years and may also have seen a change of emphasis. Charles Hadfield, the authoritative canal historian, provides a full and thought-provoking account of these issues in his book *Telford's Temptation*' (see Bibliography, page 80), but his conclusion – that Telford wanted undivided glory – are dismissed by all modern authorities.

Telford's life was so work-centred that he never married, and indeed never had a home of his own until late in his career, when he established himself in Westminster. His private life seems to have been virtually non-existent; as a young man his chief diversion was writing poetry, but that faded, although he continued to enjoy the lifelong friendship and esteem of the poet Robert Southey. His prime times were spent touring his many projects, all running concurrently in the hands of his capable deputies. Their loyalty to him speaks for Telford's character.

With due respect to William Jessop and John Rennie, both fine engineers with a high reputation but little fame, Thomas Telford was, in my opinion, the outstanding engineer of his generation. While first and foremost he must be seen as an inventive genius, he was able to combine his brilliance with the ability to remain steadfast and methodical under pressure. His pre-eminence in the new structural use of iron underpins the claim; further, the qualities that made him a leader of men, and gave him the understanding of social needs which he was in a position to help meet, ensure that he should be raised to the highest pedestal.

The Great Brunel, Tanners Yard Press, 2005

BIBLIOGRAPHY

Cameron, A.D., *The Caledonian Canal*
Cossons, N. & Trinder, B., *The Iron Bridge*
Dunlop, J., *British Fisheries Society 1786–1893*
Hadfield, C., *Thomas Telford's Temptation*
Morris, C., *On Tour with Thomas Telford*
Paxton, R. & Shipway, J., *Civil Engineering Heritage, Scotland Highlands and Islands*
Paxton, R. & Shipway, J., *Civil Engineering Heritage, Scotland Lowlands and Borders*
Rolt, L.T.C., *Thomas Telford*
Rickman, J. (ed.), *The Life of Thomas Telford*

ACKNOWLEDGEMENTS

Thanks to all who agreed to appear in this book, and to:

British Waterways, Scotland
Church of Scotland
Neil Cossons
'History Links' Museum, Dornoch
Institution of Civil Engineers
Paul Manning
Woody Morris
Pat Myhill
Michael Taylor
Tobermory Museum
Ullapool Museum
Wick Heritage Centre